ISBN 978-2-8399-3133-5

access the music, scan the QR Code or go online to https://youtu.be/Kvv_4yFqzkY

Piaf was a cat
with a unique talent:

He could sing.

2

He would sing about his adventures...

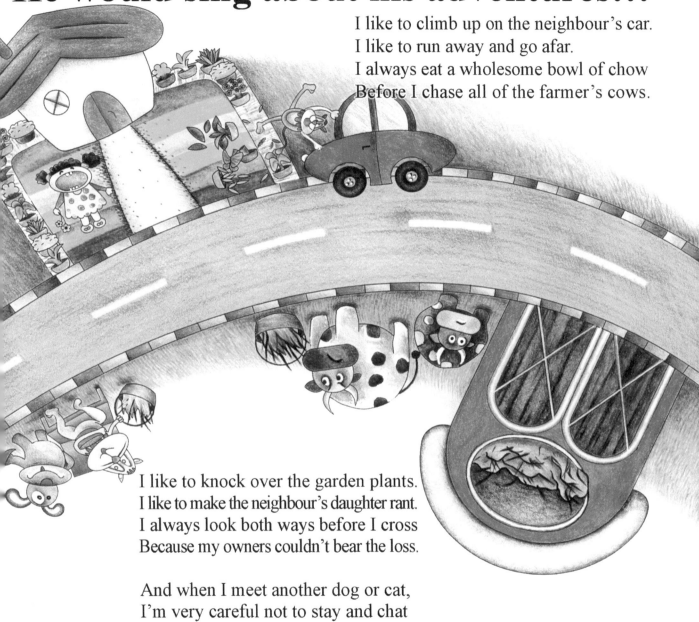

I like to climb up on the neighbour's car.
I like to run away and go afar.
I always eat a wholesome bowl of chow
Before I chase all of the farmer's cows.

I like to knock over the garden plants.
I like to make the neighbour's daughter rant.
I always look both ways before I cross
Because my owners couldn't bear the loss.

And when I meet another dog or cat,
I'm very careful not to stay and chat
Until my mommy says that it's okay
And then we play together one fine day.

3

He would sing
when he chased mice...

Oh I see a little mouse;
He's just behind that old farm house,
And if I hurry, I will beat
The falcons to the feast.
Little mouse is fast, I see;
He's climbing up an apple tree,
But felines are a faster foe,
And birds of prey too slow!

Plump and juicy:
Oh I think it's time for lunch!
Plump and juicy:
Little rodent,
crunch, crunch, crunch!
Ouch that mouse threw
Apples from the apple tree,
Wow that mouse is
Smarter than he looked to be.

**And then again,
he would sing about his questions in life.**

I know why they
call the coat that
I wear in the
rain a raincoat;
I know why they
call the snake that
makes a rattling
sound a rattlesnake,
I know that.

I know why they
call the cup-shaped
yellow flowers
little buttercups;
But I don't know
why a hungry
caterpillar that can fly
is called a butterfly.

With its colours
Unlike butter,
It just flutters
While I putter...
Pretty butterfly,
Pretty butterfly,
Why, oh why do people call you a butterfly?

7

But Piaf could not always sing.

He learnt his special skill from a very special teacher.

My mother taught me to
sing for an audience.
And I had stage fright
On stage every night

Until she left me to
Sing a capella
Without a cockatoo,
tweeting a note or two.

Now that she's gone,I
think of her always,
And with this song,the
memories live on,
and on, and on;
the memories live on!

And using
this skill to keep
time and count sheep...

Piaf, purring softly, would
sing himself
to sleep.

10

Jumping little sheep…
They help me to go to sleep.
Warm slippers,
they help me to warm my feet.
Little angels, they protect me
while I am dreaming, dreaming.

11

Scratch and the children run away.
Hiss and the other cats won't stay.
Moan and you'll moan alone with
No one to cuddle you or to play.

Smile and the world will smile with you.
Laugh and they will not dare to 'boo'.
Straighten those whiskers, meow meow,
You better smile and then take a bow.

My Dreams

My Dreams